THE ZEN OF GNASHER

meadowside
CHILDREN'S BOOKS

Fortunes exist among leftovers.

Japanese Proverb

Perseverance is a
sign of willpower.

Lao Tsu's Tao Te Ching

The world is like a mirror,
you see?
Smile and your friends
smile back.

Japanese Zen saying

Anger will never disappear so
long as thoughts of resentment
are cherished in the mind.
Anger will disappear just
as soon as thoughts of
resentment are forgotten.

Buddha

Practice non-action.
Work without doing.
Taste the tasteless.

Lao Tsu's Tao Te Ching

So an ancient once said
'attain deliverance in disturbances.'

Zen master Kyong Ho

The sage stays behind, thus he is ahead.
He is detached, thus at one with all.
Through selfless action,
he attains fulfilment.

Lao Tsu's Tao Te Ching

Do not start if afraid.
Once begun do not be afraid.

Mongolian proverb

An insincere and evil friend is more
to be feared than a wild beast.
A wild beast may wound
your body, but an evil friend
will wound your mind.

Buddha

Do not be concerned about
others not appreciating you.
Be concerned about your
not appreciating others.

Confucius

The fierce tiger is inferior
to the local worm.

Chinese Proverb

Your own dog bites your hand.

Japanese Proverb

Before receiving
there must be giving.

Lao Tsu's Tao Te Ching

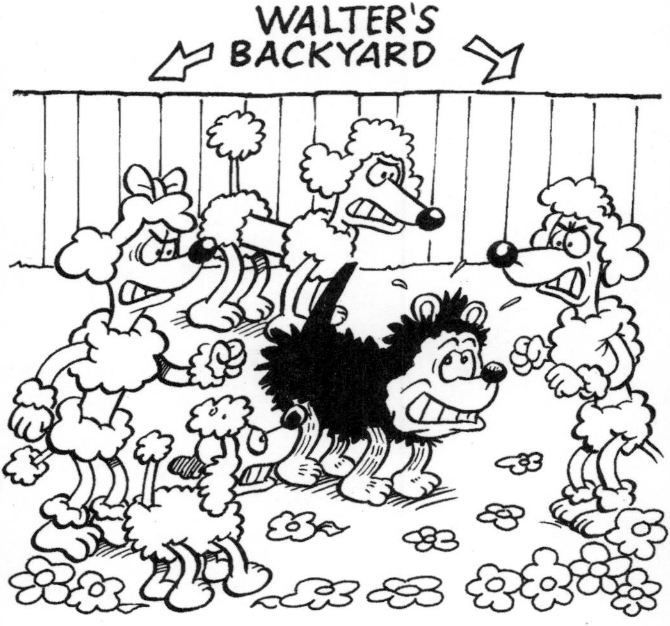
WALTER'S BACKYARD

When the tiger comes down
from the mountain to the plains,
it is bullied by the dogs.

Chinese Proverb

You cannot judge a person
from how he looks.

Chinese Proverb

I would rather be a dog in
peaceful times than live as a man
or woman in turbulent times.

Chinese Proverb

Having made a mistake, not
to correct it is a mistake indeed.

Confucius

He who is filled with virtue
is like a newborn child.
Wasps and serpents will not sting him.
Wild beasts will not pounce on him.

Lao Tsu's Tao Te Ching

Don't chase a dog into a blind alley.

Chinese Proverb

If the boss is full,
who cares about the hungry slave?

Uighur proverb

What is a joke for the cat
will be death for a mouse.

Mongolian proverb

He who knows when to stop
does not find himself in trouble.
He will stay forever safe.

Lao Tsu's Tao Te Ching

If we dig precious things from the land,
we will invite disaster.

Indian Proverb

The crafty rabbit has three
different entrances to its lair.

Chinese Proverb

Similarities call friends.

Japanese Proverb

Teaching without words
and work without doing
are only understood
by the very few.

Lao Tsu's Tao Te Ching

The more you eat,
the more you gain.

Okinawan proverb

Feed a dog for three days
and it is grateful for three years.
Feed a cat for three years
and it forgets after three days.

Japanese Proverb

Racing and hunting madden the mind.

Lao Tsu's Tao Te Ching

A pig used to dirt
turns his nose up at rice.

Japanese Proverb

When someone comes to pay compliments
and be specially helpful without cause,
he is either a crook or a thief.

Chinese Proverb

A good bark year
makes a good wheat year.

Indian proverb

He appears like a God
and disappears like a phantom.

Japanese Proverb

In dealing with others,
be gentle and kind.

Lao Tsu's Tao Te Ching

When you reach the top,
keep climbing.

Zen teaching

What we think,
we become.

Buddha

Instead of living like
a rabbit for 100 years,
live like a tiger for a day.

Uighur proverb

Men should worry about fame
just as pigs about being fat.

Chinese Proverb

People pretend to dislike
what they cannot get.

Kashmiri Proverb

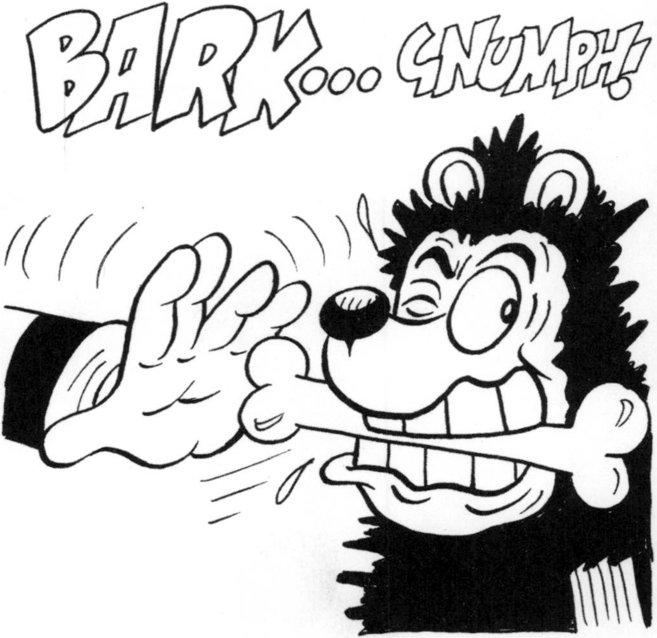
BARK... GNUMPH!

The tongue, because it has no bone,
says various things.

Assamese proverb

If a man is great, even his dog
will wear a proud look.

Japanese Proverb

When eating choose the place.
When playing choose your friends.

Kashmiri Proverb

When you go up the mountain too often,
you will eventually encounter the tiger.

Chinese Proverb

A tied dog can do no hunting.

Uighur proverb

Once the food comes,
the appreciation disappears.

Uighur proverb

A merry companion on the road
is as good as a nag.

Japanese Proverb

The leftovers of some can
be a hearty meal for others.

Kashmiri Proverb

JOIN THE BEANO CLUB. THE MEMBERSHIP IS FOR ONE YEAR AND THE BRONZE MEMBERSHIP PACK INCLUDES...

- A specially designed T-shirt, not available to buy anywhere. Gnasher clockwork chattering teeth.
- A handy tote bag— ideal for sports gear or a packed lunch.
- A frisbee with a difference. Write a message on a magic pad on the MESSAGE FRISBEE, and send it by 'airmail' to a friend and wait for their reply.
- Giant size Beano Club poster for your wall.
- A novelty practical joke.
- A Bronze membership card and a wallet to keep it safe.•A pocket - size Beano Club special with two long stories.

DURING THE YEAR YOU'LL ALSO RECEIVE...

- A special Beano Club birthday card from The Beano characters and The Beano Editor.
- Other mail sent from your pals at The Beano.
- Newsletters with competitions, news about other Beano Club members, exclusive offers for members only and inside info about what's going on with the Club or The Beano comic.
- Information about how to become a Silver Member.

PLEASE NOTE:
The contents of the Bronze pack may change from time to time. Allow up to 28 days for delivery. Membership is for one year. To join The Beano Club as a Bronze member, simply log onto

www.beanotown.com